BLUEPRINTS
Maths
Key Stage 2
Copymasters

Second edition

David and Wendy Clemson

Stanley Thornes (Publishers) Ltd

Do you receive BLUEPRINTS NEWS?

Blueprints is an expanding series of practical teacher's ideas books and photocopiable resources for use in primary schools. Books are available for separate infant and junior age ranges for every core and foundation subject, as well as for an ever widening range of other primary teaching needs. These include **Blueprints Primary English** books and **Blueprints Resource Banks**. **Blueprints** are carefully structured around the demands of National Curriculum in England and Wales, but are used successfully by schools and teachers in Scotland, Northern Ireland and elsewhere.

Blueprints provide:
- *Total curriculum coverage*
- *Hundreds of practical ideas*
- *Books specifically for the age range you teach*
- *Flexible resources for the whole school or for individual teachers*
- *Excellent photocopiable sheets – ideal for assessment and children's work profiles*
- *Supreme value*

Books may be bought by credit card over the telephone and information obtained on **(0242) 577944**. Alternatively, photocopy and return this **FREEPOST** form to receive **Blueprints News**, our regular update on all new and existing titles. You may also like to add the name of a friend who would be interested in being on the mailing list.

Please add my name to the **BLUEPRINTS NEWS** mailing list.

Mr/Mrs/Miss/Ms _____

Home address _____

_____ Postcode _____

School address _____

_____ Postcode _____

Please also send **BLUEPRINTS NEWS** to:

Mr/Mrs/Miss/Ms _____

Address _____

_____ Postcode _____

To: Marketing Services Dept., Stanley Thornes Ltd, FREEPOST (GR 782), Cheltenham, GL50 1BR

Text © David Clemson and Wendy Clemson 1995

Original line illustrations by Andrew Keylock © ST(P) Ltd 1995

The right of David and Wendy Clemson to be identified as authors of this work has been asserted by them in accordance with the Copyright, Designs and Patents Act 1988.

First published in 1992 by:
Stanley Thornes (Publishers) Ltd
Ellenborough House
Wellington Street
CHELTENHAM GL50 1YD

Reprinted 1993 (twice), 1994

Second edition 1995

A catalogue record for this book is available from the British Library.

ISBN 07487 2222 X

Typeset by Tech-Set, Gateshead, Tyne & Wear

Printed and bound in Great Britain

CONTENTS

INTRODUCTION

In this book there are 112 photocopiable worksheets. C1 to C103 are linked specifically to activities in the *Teacher's Resource Book*. RC1 to RC9 are resource copymasters and are for use again and again across all Sections of the book. Where the photocopy sheets are referred to in the text of the *Teacher's Resource Book* there are some instructions on how to use them. They are referred to by number in the *Teacher's Resource Book* by this symbol:

When the children have completed these worksheets they can be added to workfiles or used as exemplar material in pupil profiles. You may also wish to use completed worksheets as a resource for your assessments. The Record sheet (at the back of the book) is a tick list, on which you can note the photocopy sheets each child has used.

Name _____

Number collection

Numbers important to me

8
2
1
Lucky
6
7
9
Birthday
3
9
Family
5 4 3 2 1 Friends

1
999
5
8
100
2
Unlucky 13
4
11

Name _____

Round the bend game

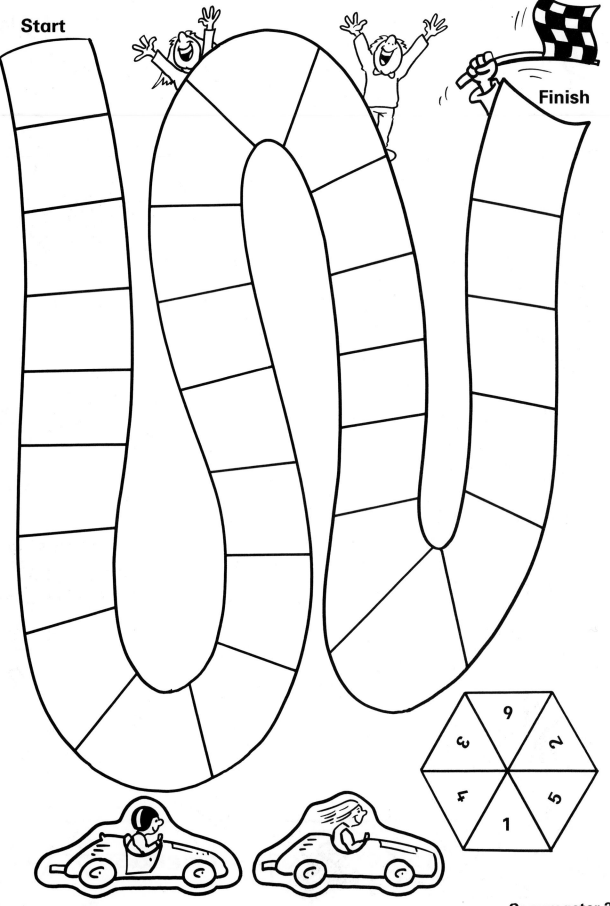

Start

Finish

Monkey gets the bananas game

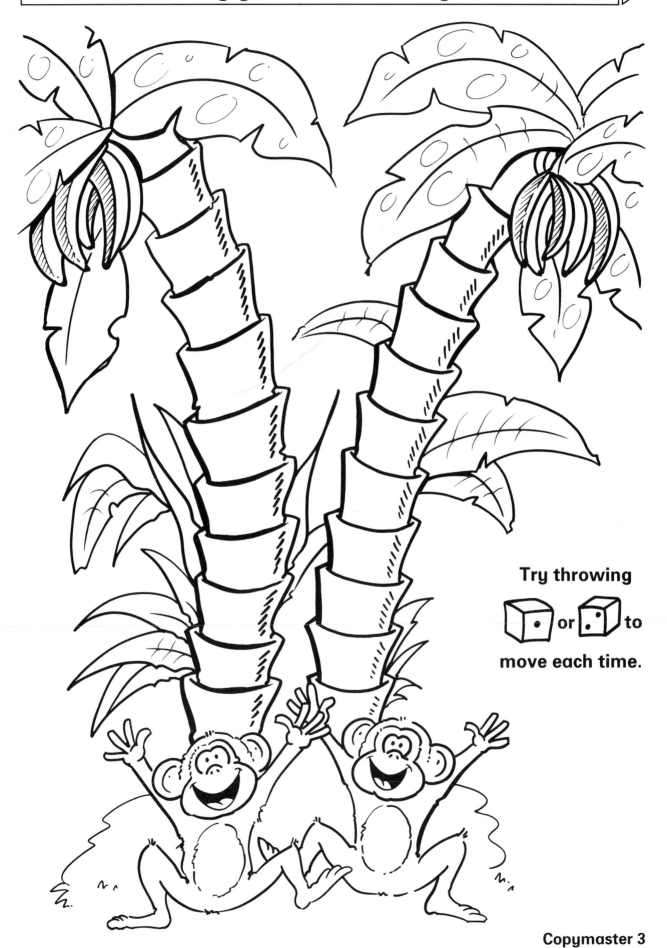

Try throwing or to move each time.

Name _____

10 × 5 half game board

Name _____

Up the aliens and down the bats!

Finish

50	49	48	47	46
41	42	43	44	45
40	39	38	37	36
31	32	33	34	35
30	29	28	27	26
21	22	23	24	25
20	19	18	17	16
11	12	13	14	15
10	9	8	7	6
1	2	3	4	5

Copymaster 5

Name _____

10s and 1s arrays

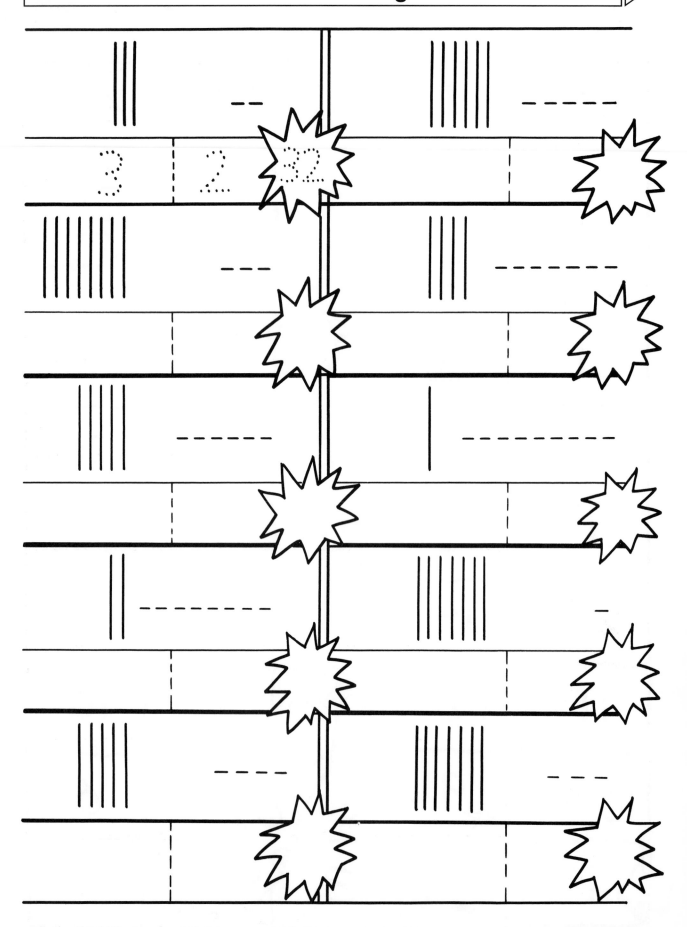

Name _____

Tens and units

Try these numbers.

Set out the tens and ones here.

28

31

85

47

56

62

79

94

Ordering numbers

Put these numbers in order

Smallest

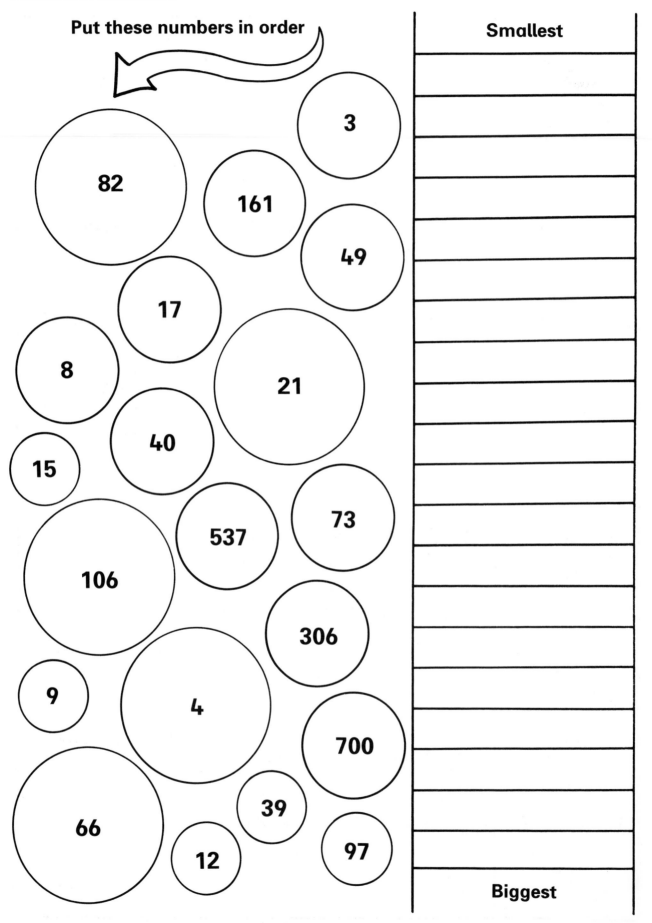

Biggest

Name _____

Place value (1)

Place value (2)

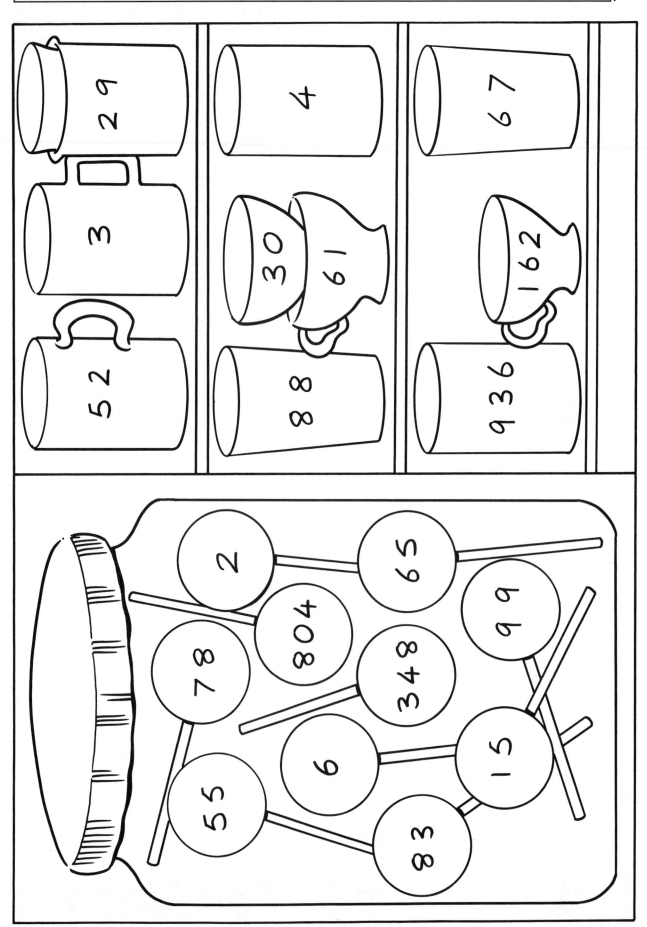

Name _____

Place value (3)

tens units			tens units			tens units			tens units				
9	9		hundreds units	1	1	units	6	0	units	2				
5	5		tens units	6		hundreds tens	9	6	tens units	8	7			
6	3		units	3	0	units	8	9	units	6	5			
8	8		units	4	3	hundreds tens	2	5	units	4				
6	8		units	6	3	hundreds	5		tens	1				
4	8		tens	3	9	units	1	1	hundreds	8	units	6		
3	4		hundreds	9	8	tens	7	3	tens	3	2			
8	0		tens	2	9	units	4	2	units	6	3			
hundreds tens	2	8	units	3	2	units	9	1	tens	0	6			
units	7	8	units	5	2	tens	6	7	units	1	0			
tens units	5	7	tens	5	5	tens	6	9	hundreds tens	1	6			
tens	5	5	tens	1		tens	6	2	tens	3		units	9	9

Name _____

Function machines

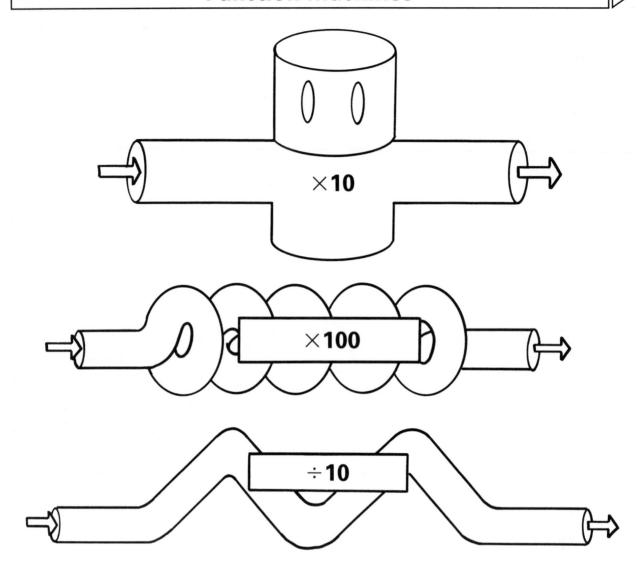

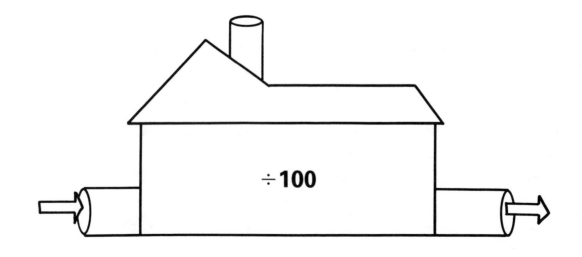

Number bases

From an aboriginal dialect in Australia:

One mal   **Four bularr-bularr**
Two bularr   **Five bularr-guliba**
Three guliba   **Six guliba-guliba**

(Discrete number words for one, two, three – then two-two, two-three, three-three.)

Toba tribesmen of Paraguay use:

One nathedac   **Six cacayni-cacaynilia**
Two cacayni or nivoca   **Seven nathedac-cacayni-cacaynilia**
Three cacaynilia   **Eight nivoca-nalotapegat**
Four nalotapegat   **Nine nivoca-nalotapegat-nathedac**
Five nivoca-cacaynilia   **Ten cacayni-nivoca-nalotapegat**

Discrete number words up to four – then a mix of addition and multiplication:

two-three   **two fours**
two-threes   **two fours (and) one**
one (and) two threes   **two (and) two fours**

Some South American Indians use finger counting. Number words follow this pattern:

One   **Hand-one**   **Two-hands-one**
Two   **Hand-two**   **and so on.**
Three   **Hand-three**
Four   **Hand-four**
Hand   **Two-hands**

Source: Flegg G., Numbers: Their History and Meaning, 1983

Numbers using base two

128	64	32	16	8	4	2	1	Number to be set out
	Look at this one 1	0	1	0	1	1		43

Now try these

128	64	32	16	8	4	2	1	
								7
								62
								100
								17
								222
								59
								28
								97
								112
								80
								171

Shop window

Shop window

Bargains! Shop here! Open today

Name _____

Expedition kit price list

	Price		Price
Sleeping bag		Soup, per tin (serves 4)	
Tent (sleeps 4)		Baked beans (large)	
Cooking stove		Bread (loaf)	
Gas		Biscuits (pack)	
Water bottle		Fruit juice (litre)	
Camp cook pots (3)		Milk (pint)	
Mug/bowl/knife/fork/spoon set		Cheese (pound)	
Compass		Sausages (pound)	
Torch (needs 2 batteries)		Tinned fruit (large)	
Batteries for torch (pack of 2)		Porridge	
First aid kit		Eggs (×6)	
Waterproof cagoul		Rice (pound)	
Jogsuit (unisex)		Potatoes (pound)	
Size S (7–8)		Tomatoes (pound)	
Size M (8–9)		Carrots (pound)	
Size L (9–11)		Bananas (pound)	
Wellies		Apples (pound)	
Sizes 12–3, per pair		Extra items:	
Sizes 4 or more, per pair			
Trainers			
Sizes 12–3, per pair			
Sizes 4 or more, per pair			
Tea towel			
Washing-up liquid			
Cleaning cloth			

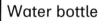

Name _____

Expedition kit special offers

1

All clothing £1 off this week.

2

Everything half price.

3

Tents 25% off.

4

All camping equipment 10% off normal price.

5

Baked beans – 5 tins for the price of 4. Buy 4, get 1 Free

6

Pack of 6 cleaning cloths free with 2 bottles of washing-up liquid.

7

Potatoes £1 a 10 lb bag. Special bargain

Use one or more offers in your calculations.

Copymaster 17

Name _____

Half

Colour half

Draw half

Half a face   **Half a coin**

Half a triangle   **Half a chocolate bar**

Name _____

Quarter

Cut into quarters

Apple pie

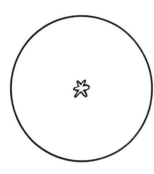
Orange

Check flag

Draw a quarter of these:

A quarter of a plate

A quarter of a table

A quarter of a leaf

A quarter of a handkerchief

Name _____

Equivalent fractions

$\frac{2}{4}$

$\frac{3}{4}$

$\frac{1}{3}$

$\frac{4}{8}$

$\frac{6}{8}$

$\frac{12}{16}$

$\frac{2}{6}$

$\frac{1}{4}$

$\frac{8}{16}$

$\frac{4}{16}$

$\frac{4}{12}$

$\frac{1}{2}$

$\frac{2}{12}$

$\frac{2}{8}$

$\frac{1}{6}$

$\frac{8}{24}$

Use a different colour to join together each chain of equivalent fractions!

Copymaster 20

Name _____

Equivalent fractions strings

Make patterns of equivalent fractions

½

⅓

¼

⅓

⅕

¹⁄₁₂
¹⁄₁₀
⅛
⅙
⅕
¼
⅓
½

¾

²⁄₄

¹⁄₈

¹⁄₁₀

²⁄₆

Name _____

Ratio drawing

Draw a picture of yourself using a ratio 1:12 cm.
Before you start estimate how much of the paper you will take up.

Whatever happened to you child?

I got my ratios wrong Miss!

Copymaster 22

Reporter's pad

Name of reporter _____

Working for _____ (name of magazine)

Report on _____

Date _____ **Time** _____

Name of interviewee (if any) _____

Reporting from _____ (location)

Strip sums

Make 10	0 + ☐
Cut out strips.	Staple] together.
☐ + 9	1 + ☐
☐ + 8	2 + ☐
☐ + 7	3 + ☐
☐ + 6	4 + ☐
☐ + 5	5 + ☐
☐ + 4	6 + ☐
☐ + 3	7 + ☐
☐ + 2	8 + ☐
☐ + 1	9 + ☐
☐ + 0	10 + ☐

Odds and evens quizzes

Colour odd numbers yellow, even numbers green.

Function problems

$x = y + 3$

    if x = 10   y =

    if x = 12   y =

    if x = 6   y =

$x = 4y$

    if x = 4   y =

    if x = 12   y =

    if x = 20   y =

$x = \dfrac{y}{2}$

    If x = 10   y =

    If x = 30   y =

    If x = 24   y =

$x = \dfrac{y}{2}$

Enter values for x

y	x	y	x	y	x
1		6		11	
2		7		12	
3		8		13	
4		9		14	
5		10		15	

$x = 2y + 1$

    if x = 5   y =

    if x = 9   y =

    if x = 19   y =

$x = 2y + 1$

Enter values for x

y	x	y	x	y	x
1		7		13	
2		8		14	
3		9		15	
4		10		16	
5		11		17	
6		12		18	

Copymaster 26

Addition to 10

Try these

add   make

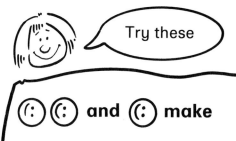

buttons

Now these...

How are you doing?

What do you think?
Good work?

seven and two...

two and eight...

one and three...

eight and one...

nine and two...

six and three...

five and two...

three and five...

four and four...

one and six...

$7 + 2 =$

$5 + 5 =$

$3 + 6 =$

$1 + 8 =$

$5 + 2 =$

$4 + 4 =$

$3 + 5 =$

$2 + 1 + 1 =$

$1 + 3 + 2 =$

Subtraction to 10

Make  pop! disappear

5 take away 【2】 leaves

6 take away 【3】 leaves

8 take away 【5】 leaves

9 take away 【4】 leaves

four minus 【two】

five minus 【three】

two minus 【one】

six minus 【five】

9 − 【5】 = ☐   8 − 【6】 = ☐

10 − 【4】 = ☐   6 − 【4】 = ☐

7 − 【3】 = ☐   3 − 【1】 = ☐

5 − 【2】 = ☐   2 − 【1】 = ☐

4 − 【1】 = ☐   4 − 【3】 = ☐

Copymaster 28

Name _____

Number bonds to 20: Bingo

7	3	15	10
1	12	5	9
18	4	16	2
8	6	11	14

16	12	7	1
10	8	2	15
13	14	4	19
5	18	3	9

11	5	14	18
19	15	6	1
17	9	2	8
3	4	10	13

2	4	11	6
7	1	19	13
16	5	3	9
10	8	12	17

Add/subtract to 20 check

Please check these sums ✓ or ✗

13 + 2 + 1 = 16   17 − 6 = 11

8 + 4 = 12   17 − 7 = 9

7 + 12 = 19   11 − 2 − 1 = 8

5 + 5 + 6 = 16   5 − 2 = 3

10 + 5 = 14   18 − 6 = 12

20 − 6 − 6 = 8   7 − 3 = 4

15 + 3 = 18   5 + 13 = 18

8 + 3 = 11   4 − 1 = 3

6 + 5 = 11   3 + 3 + 3 = 9

Did you spot the sums that were wrong?

Copymaster 30

Multiplication facts

12 3×4 4×3 6×2 2×6

Can you do these?

10

6

25

12

9

60

16

8

Number patterns

1, 3, 5, 7, 9,   ___ , ___ , ___ , ___

10, 20, 30, 40,   ___ , ___ , ___ , ___

80, 75, 70, 65,   ___ , ___ , ___

Continue the pattern.

These are no problem. Look for PATTERN.

4, 8, 12, 16,   ___ , ___ , ___ , ___

36, 33, 30, 27,   ___ , ___ , ___ , ___

62, 68, 74, 80,   ___ , ___ , ___ , ___

1, 2, 4, 8,   ___ , ___ , ___ , ___

0, 5, 10, 15, 20,   ___ , ___ , ___ , ___

0, 9, 18, 27, 36,   ___ , ___ , ___ , ___

Copymaster 32

Maze game (1)

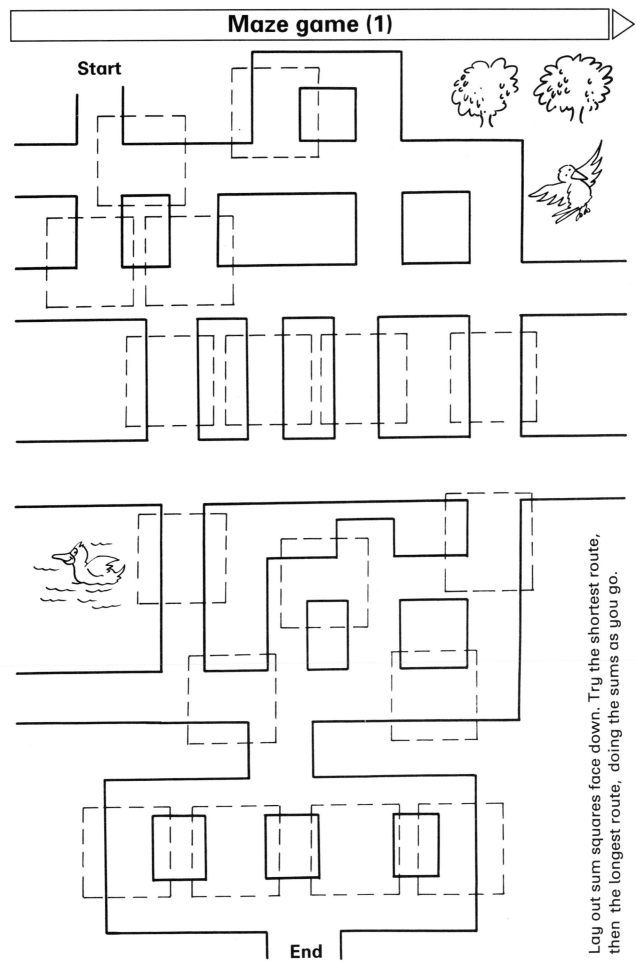

Start

End

Lay out sum squares face down. Try the shortest route, then the longest route, doing the sums as you go.

Name

Maze game (2)

$4 + 8 + 3$ $+ 5 + 7$ $+ 2$	$5 + 7 + 2$ $+ 1 + 6$ $+ 1 + 3$	$62 - 50$	$311 - 34$	$763 - 16$	$634 - 170$	$881 - 316$
$1 + 3 + 5$ $+ 7 + 9$ $+ 4$	$9 + 2 + 4$ $+ 5 + 7$ $+ 8$	$332 + 63$	$579 - 58$	$249 - 61$	$91 + 23$	$150 + 324$
$671 - 286$	$316 - 166$	$855 - 332$	$155 + 225$	$147 - 416$	$607 - 86$	$361 + 416$
12×6	17×7	41×6	11×6	60×3	41×4	41×9
60×5	$55 \div 5$	$47 \div 6$	41×5	$22 \div 7$	$93 \div 8$	$20 \div 3$
$62 \div 5$	$46 \div 2$	$75 \div 5$	$89 \div 2$			

Stick onto card before cutting out. Blank tiles are for additional sums for use on home-made mazes.

Mental arithmetic cards

5 × 111 555	325 ÷ 5 65	121 ÷ 11 11
62 ÷ 2 31	24 × 8 192	36 × 12 432
522 + 212 734	456 + 47 903	219 + 27 446
368 − 40 328	747 − 115 632	94 − 61 33
483 + 402 885	804 − 140 664	230 ÷ 5 46

Box for cards

Fold in

Glue flap

Glue flap

Fold in

Fold in

Glue flap

Glue flap

Fold in

Puzzle page

Addition squares

+	2	5	10
2			
5			
10			

+	4	6	8
2			
4			
6			

+	3	4	5
6			
7			
8			

Multiplication squares

×	1	2	3
1			
2			
3			

×	2	4	6
8			
10			
12			

×	1	3	5
7			
9			
11			

Copymaster 39

Typical calendar month

Sunday	1	8	15	22	29
Monday	2	9	16	23	30
Tuesday	3	10	17	24	31
Wednesday	4	11	18	25	
Thursday	5	12	19	26	
Friday	6	13	20	27	
Saturday	7	14	21	28	

Name _____

Multiplication/division methods

We are trying to collect as many methods as we can for doing multiplication and division sums. Please can you help us by writing down, step by step, the method you use, explaining each step as you go.

Here are two sample sums to work on: 219×35
$936 \div 78$

Thank you for your help.

Copymaster 41

Division by 2, 5, 10

Ring in red the numbers divisible by 2, in blue the numbers divisible by 5 and in green the numbers divisible by 10.

16   450   733

500   76   80 60

50   31   456

24   102   7,000

4
    35   200
                        100

Name _____

Missing numbers

How many missing?

☐ cakes to make 8

☐ children to make 9

☐ children to make 10

☐ bananas to make 5

☐ beads to make 9

☐ pups to make 7

☐ chips to make 7

☐ chicks to make 6

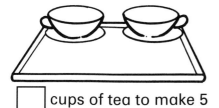

☐ cups of tea to make 5

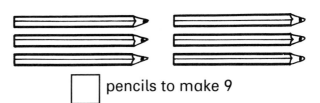

☐ pencils to make 9

Function machines (1)

An add 5 machine

6 → [+ 5] →

15 → [+ 5] →

12 → [+ 5] →

→ [+ 5] → 8

→ [+ 5] → 17

→ [+ 5] → 20

→ [+ 5] → 13

Name _____

Function machines (2)

The −7 robot

17 ➡ −7 ➡ 10

This one is done for you.
Now do some more.

Function machines (3)

'Nogard' chase . . . . . .

The 'Lufdaerd Nogards' (dreadful dragons). Did you emerge OK?

Name _____

Function machines (4)

What are the machines doing?

IN		OUT

16 — 4

10 — 10

6 — 36

29 — 11

77 — 23

7 — 15

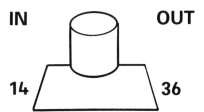

27 — 3

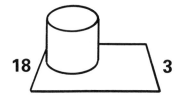

22 — 44

IN		OUT

14 — 36

18 — 3

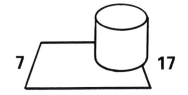

7 — 17

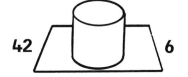

42 — 6

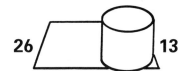

26 — 13

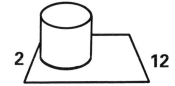

2 — 12

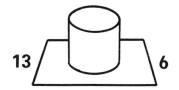

13 — 6

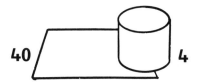

40 — 4

Copymaster 47

Function machines (5)

Use this second sheet of information to find out what the machines are doing.

IN   OUT   IN   OUT

 20 → 5
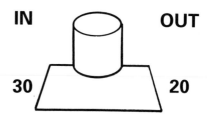 30 → 20

 25 → 4
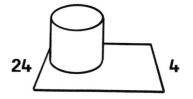 24 → 4

 3 → 9
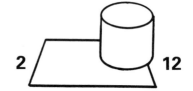 2 → 12

 44 → 8
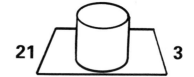 21 → 3

 26 → 74
 86 → 43

 2 → 5
 5 → 15

 90 → 10
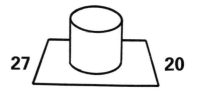 27 → 20

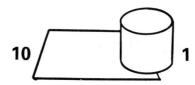 14 → 28
 10 → 1

Fractions and percentages (1)

Solve these

$\frac{1}{5}$ of £130 = ☐

10% of 62g

$\frac{3}{8}$ of 384 cm = ☐

90% of £890

$\frac{1}{2}$ of 67.2 ml = ☐

4.5% of 90 m/s ☐

$\frac{7}{10}$ of 1 hour = ☐

70% of 3 hours ☐

$\frac{1}{4}$ of 763 m = ☐

63% of 972 cm

$\frac{1}{6}$ of 12.66 mins = ☐

12% of 15 minutes

$\frac{1}{9}$ of 652.5g = ☐

1% of 1000g

$\frac{5}{6}$ of 0.06 mm = ☐

20.75% of 530 cm

Name _____

Fractions and percentages (2)

Solve these

$\frac{3}{10}$ of £560 = ☐   5% of 50g ☐

$\frac{2}{5}$ of 562 cm = ☐   20% of £5000 ☐

$\frac{1}{3}$ of 0.66 cm = ☐   7.5% of 80 m ☐

$\frac{1}{4}$ of a minute = ☐   15% of 3 hours ☐

$\frac{4}{5}$ of 85g = ☐   80% of 685 ml ☐

$\frac{1}{2}$ of £7.54 = ☐   30.5% of 3050g ☐

$\frac{8}{9}$ of 11.29 ml = ☐   50% of 0.05 secs ☐

$\frac{1}{12}$ of £76 = ☐   12% of £50 ☐

Shopping problems

Name _____

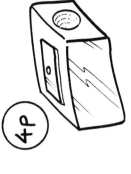

Pencil sharpener — 4p

rubber — 3p

crayon — 1p

1 crayon and 1 rubber cost ... p

1 crayon and 1 sharpener cost ... p

1 rubber and 1 sharpener cost ... p

2 crayons and 1 rubber cost ... p

2 rubbers and 1 sharpener cost ... p

2 sharpeners and 1 crayon cost ... p

3 rubbers and 2 crayons cost ... p

4 crayons and 2 rubbers cost ... p

5 crayons and 1 sharpener cost ... p

1 sharpener, 1 rubber and 2 crayons cost ... p

Cherry bun — 2p

Cake slice — 3p

1 cake slice costs ... p

2 cake slices cost ... p

3 cake slices cost ... p

1 cherry bun costs ... p

2 cherry buns cost ... p

3 cherry buns cost ... p

4 cherry buns cost ... p

5 cherry buns cost ... p

Shop contents

Name _____

Purse	Rubber	Pencil	Pen	Crayons
Pencil sharpener	Ink	Guitar sticker	Badge	Monster
Tiny hedgehog	Eye mask	Marbles	Aircraft	Knight
Doll	Notebook	Ruler	Tiny ted	Giant felt tip
Flicker book	Tiny pig	Paper and envelopes	Paint box	Felt tips
Pencil case	Monster	Tiny picture frame	Sticker	Badge

Shop prices

1p Our price	2p	3p	5p	10p
15p	18p	On offer 20p	25p	Bargain 50p
30p	11p	80p	13p	66p
4p	6p	7p	8p	9p
12p	14p	16p	17p Reduction	19p
35p	1p	2p	3p	5p

Name

Number stories

Ali had three sticker albums with 5 cards in each. He also had copies of 4 stickers which he shared between 2 friends. They gave him the same number of stickers in return. 'Now I am only 1 short of my target', he said. How many did he want to get?

We are the champions.

5 friends have 10 marbles each. What is the size of each share if they share all these between 10 people? 2 people? If 20 marbles get lost how many each can the 5 friends have?

Name _____

Problems using measures (1)

Timber shelving comes in stock lengths. How many planks of which lengths are needed to make a set of shelves of these lengths?

1 shelf 1 m 30 cm   1 shelf 1 m
1 shelf 75 cm   3 shelves 30 cm
1 shelf 60 cm

Flour and sugar come in 1 k bags. How many bags are needed for these recipes

Bread   Jam
36 loaves 20 large   40 lb jars (   )g
when   16 small   There is
flour makes   of fruit
large   and the proportions are
small

It takes 2 m 80 cm to make a shirt.
How many complete metres would we need to make

3 shirts ☐   5 shirts ☐   12 shirts ☐

Problems using measures (2)

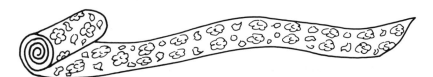

Wallpaper comes in rolls $1\frac{1}{2}$ feet wide and 33 feet long.
How many rolls are needed for a room 10 feet by 12 feet with one doorway. (Ignore the windows).

The room is 8 feet from floor to ceiling.

A helping of instant mashed potato is 20 g. A pack makes 60 g. How many packs must we buy for

4 people ☐   6 people ☐   9 people ☐

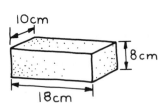

10cm

8cm

18cm

Bricks are sold in thousands. How many bricks of this size have to be bought to build a wall 7 m 20 cm height and approximately

10 m long? ☐

Name _____

Addition and subtraction – problems

An eggbox holds 6 eggs. 2 are left. How many eaten?

4 birds in a nest. 2 fly away. How many left?

**10 boys. 5 have school dinners.
How many go home for dinner?**

8 toys in the shop. 2 are sold. How many left?

3 pens. I buy 3 more. How many altogether?

**5 buds on a flower. 3 buds open.
How many still to open?**

**4 cakes on a plate. Set out 4 more.
How many altogether?**

6 buttons on a coat. 3 pop off. How many left?

Addition and subtraction – stories

Once upon a time there were 4 children. Mum called 1 in for

tea. Then there were ☐. Another 3 children joined the game.

Then there were ☐. 2 went off to the shops. Then there were ☐.

1 went home to watch TV. Then there were ☐. 2 went to get

their bikes. How many left? ☐

10 marbles to start

Lose 1

Borrow 1

Give away 5

Win 2

Buy 2

Break 3

Lose 2 more

Find 1   ☐ to finish

Name _____

Maths links

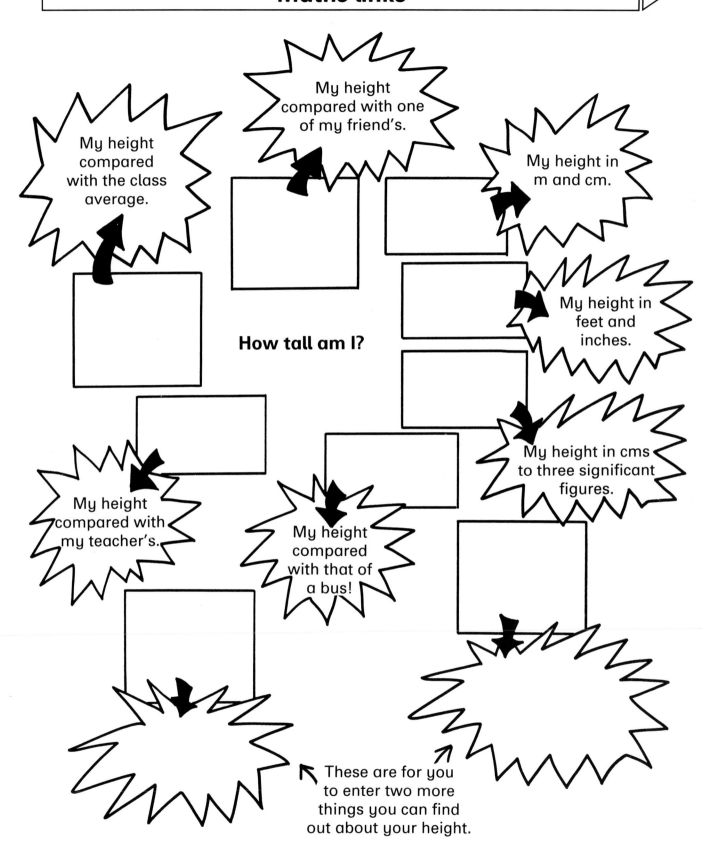

My height compared with one of my friend's.

My height compared with the class average.

My height in m and cm.

How tall am I?

My height in feet and inches.

My height in cms to three significant figures.

My height compared with my teacher's.

My height compared with that of a bus!

These are for you to enter two more things you can find out about your height.

In each of the empty boxes ☐ write all the maths activities you can do.
Here are some possibilities:

estimate • measure • calculate • find the ratio • find the fraction •
use decimals • use a calculator.

Copymaster 59

Maths link blank

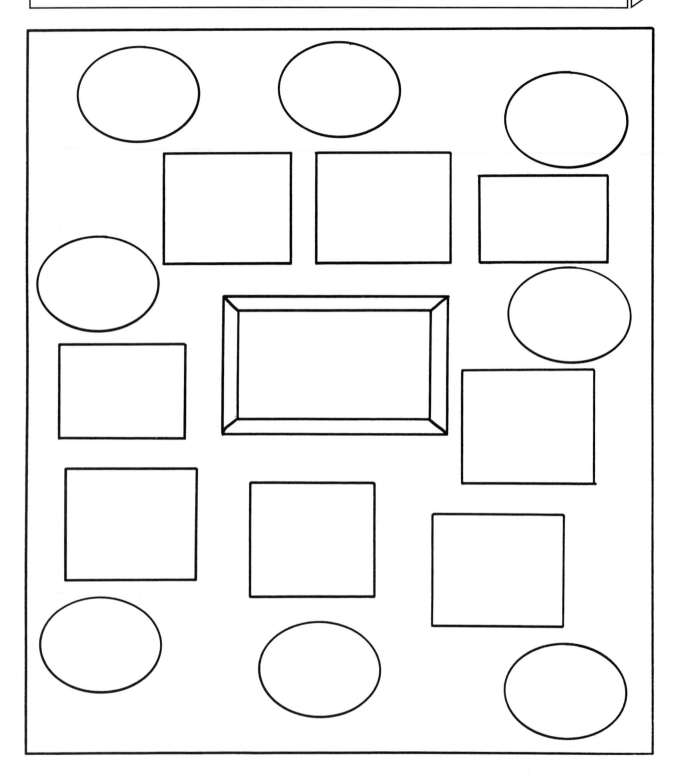

	The big issue
	Things to find out
	Ways to find out

Ratio drawings

To draw a square with the ratio 1:2 to square A

Z

A

0
0

1   Find the midpoint of the horizontal axis.
2   Draw a vertical line at that point
3   Draw a line from point Z through the origin (0,0).
4   Draw lines from all four corners of A through the origin.
Draw in the scaled down square.

Copymaster 61

Areas of rectangles

Areas of rectangles (They are twice as long as they are wide.)

Area	Length	Breadth
2 cm²		
4.5 cm²		
6 cm²		
12.5 cm²		
18 cm²		

Areas of rectangles (They are $2\frac{1}{2}$ times as long as they are wide.)

Area	Length	Breadth
17.5 cm²		
10 cm²		
2.5 cm²		

Name _____

Shape book cover

This book belongs to ....

Suky Square

Roddy Rectangle

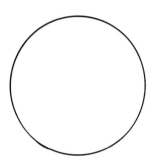

Celia Circle

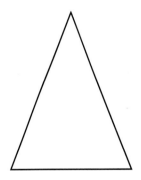

.... **Triangle**

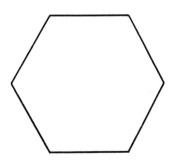

Harry Hexagon

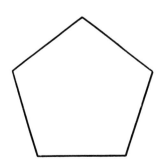

Poppy Pentagon

Copymaster 63

Quadrilaterals

Quadrilaterals:

are 2–D ✓

have 4 sides ✓

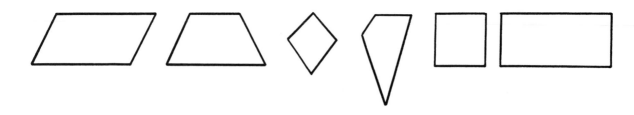

Some quadrilaterals I have seen:

Rectangles and squares ▷

Rectangles:

are 'special' quadrilaterals ✓
are 2-D ✓
have 4 sides ✓
have 2 pairs of matching sides ✓
have 4 corners the same ✓

Some rectangles I have seen:

Squares are 'special' rectangles:
have all sides the same length ✓

Some squares I have seen:

Name _____

Circles and ovals

Circles and ovals:
are 2-D ✓

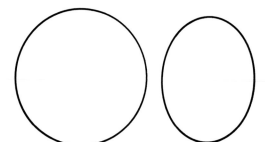

Where I have seen circles:

Where I have seen ovals:

Name _____

Triangles

Triangles:
are 2-D ✓
have 3 sides ✓

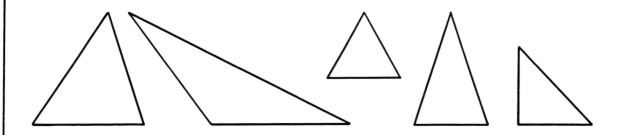

Triangles can have - all sides of different lengths
- 2 sides of the same length
- 3 sides of the same length.

Triangles I have spotted:

Hexagons and pentagons

Hexagons:
are 2-D ✓
have 6 sides ✓

Pentagons:
are 2-D ✓
have 5 sides ✓

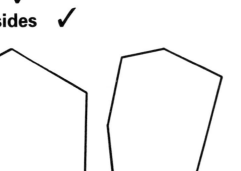

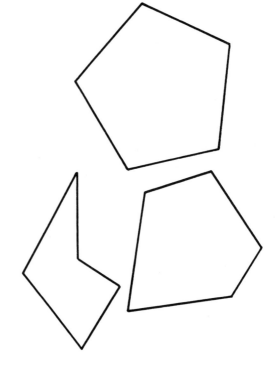

These shapes are harder to spot.

Where I have seen them:

Name _____

2-D shapes

What is this shape called?

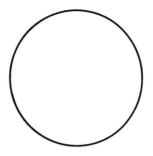

....

How many sides has a triangle? ....

What would you call a quadrilateral with 2 pairs of matching sides and right angles at the corners? ....

How many sides has a pentagon? ....

How many corners has a square? ....

What is this shape called?

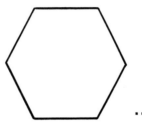

....

Draw 3 different triangles.

Cubes and cuboids

 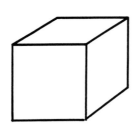 

Facts about cuboids:

What is special about a cube?

Cuboids and cubes I know:

Name _____

Cylinders

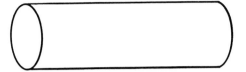

Facts about cylinders:

Cylinders I know:

Name _____

Right angles

Mark the right angles ⌐ and make them into stick men.

Name _____

Sorts quiz

Find the odd one out in each group and mark it. Why is it odd?

Does a pentagon fit a set of five- and six-sided shapes?   **Yes/No**

Does a rectangle fit a set of quadrilaterals?   **Yes/No**

Does a square go with circles or rectangles?

_____

What do you call a set of shapes which have six sides?

_____

What will a set of right-angled shapes contain?

_____

Shape challenge

Draw some rough designs.
Choose one as the basis for the final effort.

Report on shapes and angles used.

Evaluation.

Name _____

Similarity and congruence

Find and join the shapes that are congruent.
Circle and colour to match those that are similar.

Name _____

Mirror play

Make a pair of shoes, a whole cake and lots more.

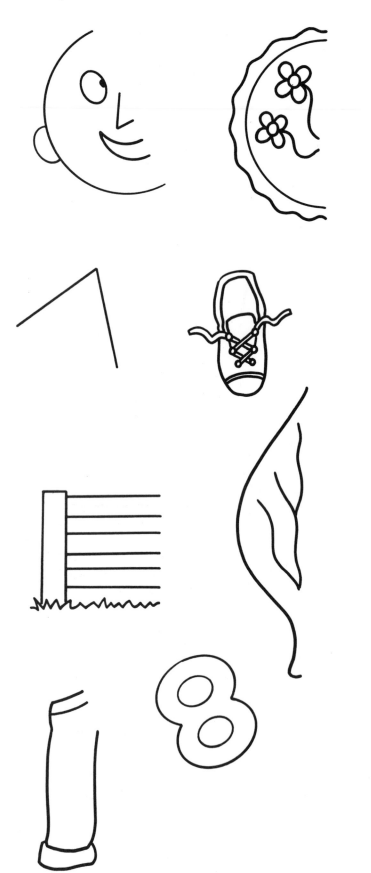
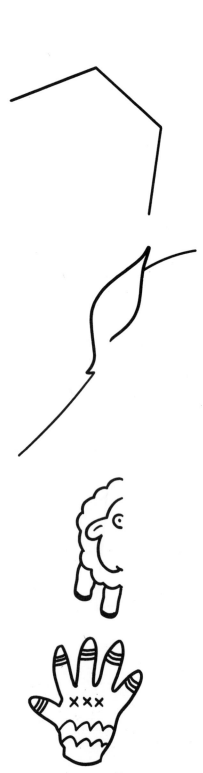

Rotational symmetry

Name _____

Shape, space & measures: reflective and rotational symmetries

Symmetry trail

What	Where	Shapes noted	Kind(s) of symmetry Be a symmetry spotter	Discussion points – lines/planes, etc.

Copymaster 78

Name _____

Tessellation record

Starter shape

What I did to the shape. Draw what was removed and where it was placed.
I used reflection ✓✗, rotation ✓✗, translation ✓✗ (ring what you used).

The final pattern

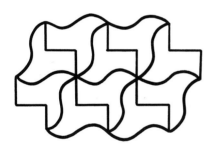

City map

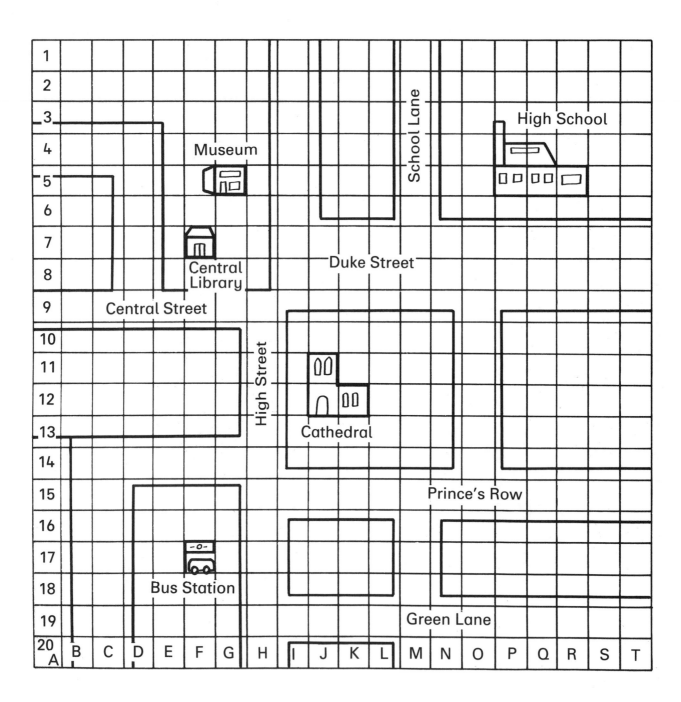

Put in more street names and important buildings.

Write a guide for visitors, or a city trail giving directions.

Name _____

Time sheet

tick tick tick tick tick tick tick

| Time sheet for _____ (date) |
| _____ (name) |

Time	What I did

Time conversion

Analogue	Digital
25 past 6	
Quarter to twelve	

Digital	Analogue
7:25	
15:45	
12:05	
23:15	
1:30	

Name _____

Measures used in jobs ▷

In the course of your work, whether at home or outside it, you probably need to use a number of measures. They may be measures of length, height, area, capacity (volume), 'weight' or time. They may be imperial measures, such as inches, pints and pounds or metric measures, such as metres and kilos.

Please can you tell us what measures you use, what you use them for and what your work is?

Name   **My work**

Measures I use

What I use these measures for

Thank you for your help.
Copymaster 83

Name _____

Squared area drawings

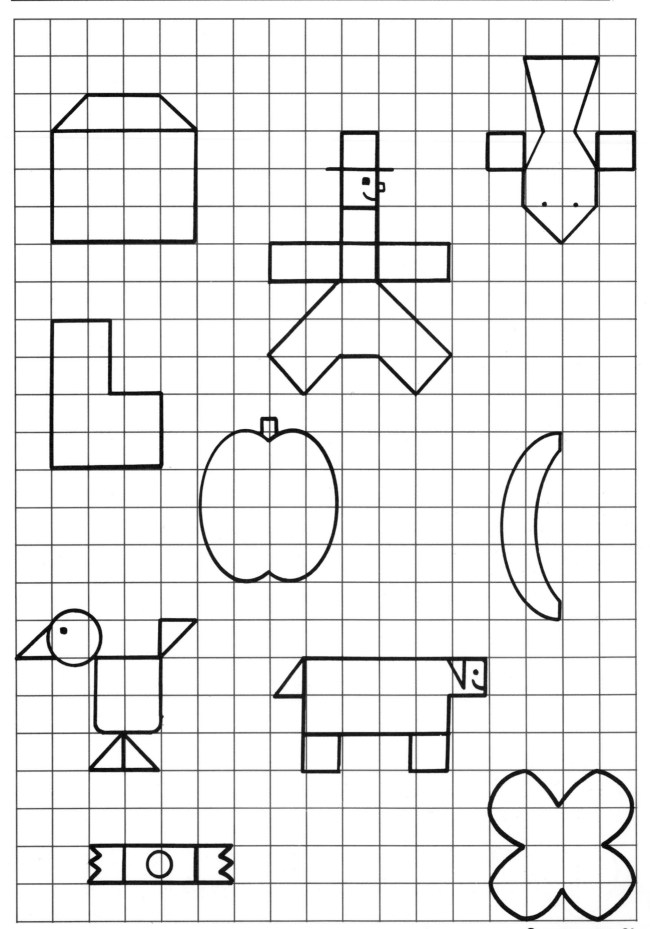

Areas of rectangles and squares

Length	Breadth	Area
11.50 cm		63.84 cm²
	63 cm	4914 cm²
12.05 cm	83.20 cm	
99.9 cm	22.2 cm	
12 miles		144 sq miles
0.632 cm	0.129 cm	
100 yds	100 yds	
	45.9 cm	3359.9 cm² (to 1 decimal place)
	11 inches	363 sq inches
357 cm		56,763 cm²
123 inches	123 inches	
5 miles		27,500 sq miles

Copymaster 85

Areas of triangles

Base	Height	Area
31.5 mm	65 mm	
12.04 cm		90.4 cm² (to 3 sig figs)
2.30 inches	7.89 inches	
56 feet		2464 sq feet
	1000 mm	50,000 mm²
7.1 cm	9.3 cm	
44 cm		726 cm²
19.92 cm		209.06 cm² (to 2 decimal places)
	60 cm	360 cm²
2.367 cm	13.001 cm	
54 cm		1755 cm²
3.336 inches		10.42 sq inches

Name _____

The Königsberg Bridge problem

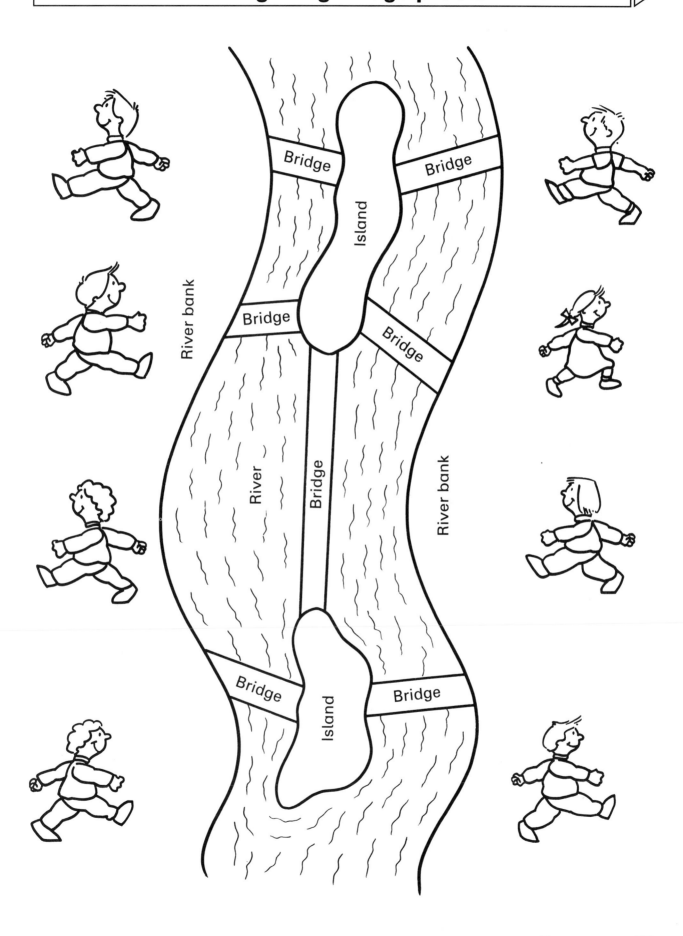

Networks

Which of these can you traverse?

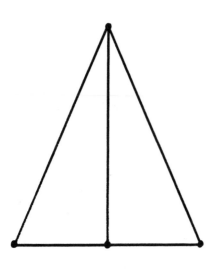
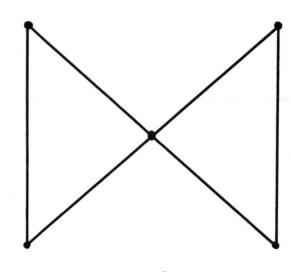

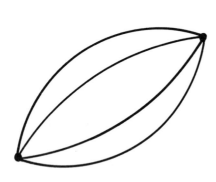
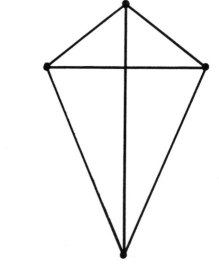

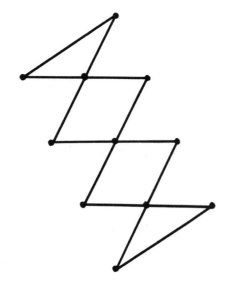
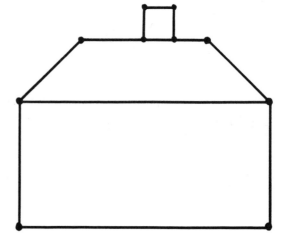

Name _____

Lists

Make four lists

Apples

Sandra

Pink

Denmark

Buttercup

Stella

Sonia

Selina

Pineapple

Daffodil

Freesia

Chile

Dandelion

Norway

Portugal

Daisy

Crocus

Sheila

Oranges

Pears

Susan

Peony

Sharon

Sarah

Malta

Snowdrop

Shirley

Brazil

Bananas

Rose

Snapdragon

Sophia

Chrysanthemum

Sylvia

Tulip

Copymaster 89

Name _____

Tables

Make a table

A cube has 6 faces, 8 corners or vertices.

A cuboid has 6 faces, 8 vertices.

A triangular prism has 5 faces, 6 vertices.

A cylinder has 3 faces, 0 vertices.

A hexagonal prism has 8 faces, 12 vertices.

Make a table from this information!

Tom has 3 sisters, 1 brother,

Cheryl has 4 brothers, 1 half brother.

Zita has 1 twin sister.

Gerry has 1 sister, 2 brothers.

Louise has 2 sisters, 2 half sisters.

Benedict is an only child.

Daphne has 1 brother.

Manley has 2 brothers.

Stephan has 1 sister, 1 brother.

Name _____

Tally

Information about ....

....

Record of	Number of times
....	
....	
....	

When we finish the tallying we can put it in our neat books.

Frequency charts

Number of days in the month the sun shines.

	Mondays	|||
	Tuesdays	|||||
	Wednesdays	||
	Thursdays	|||
	Fridays	||
	Saturdays	||
	Sundays	|||||

Number of times books on these topics borrowed in a week.

Wild animals	||||||||||||||
Pets	||||||
Farm animals	|||
Puppets	||||||||||
Space	||||||||||||||||||

Copymaster 92

Name _____

Block graph

Foods we hate: 20 children chose the two foods they dislike most from the list.

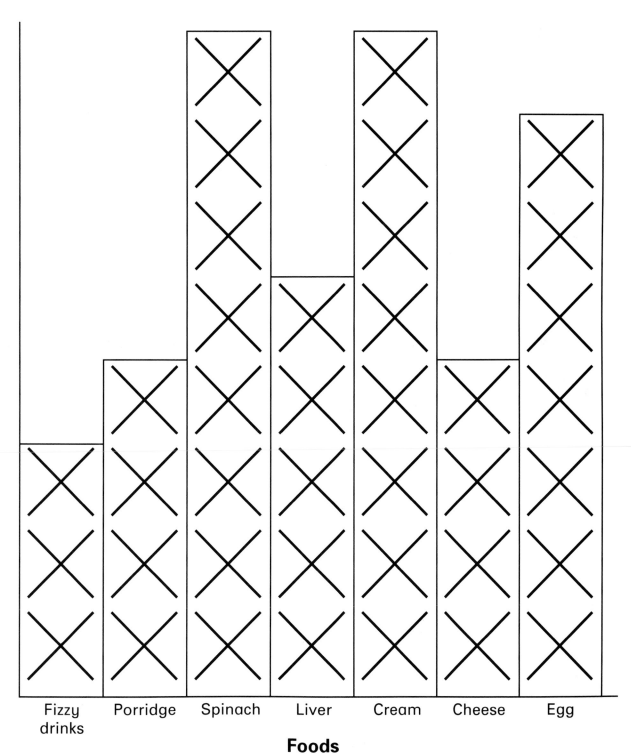

Number of children

Fizzy drinks   Porridge   Spinach   Liver   Cream   Cheese   Egg

Foods

Bar charts

Number of passengers on the buses in a week

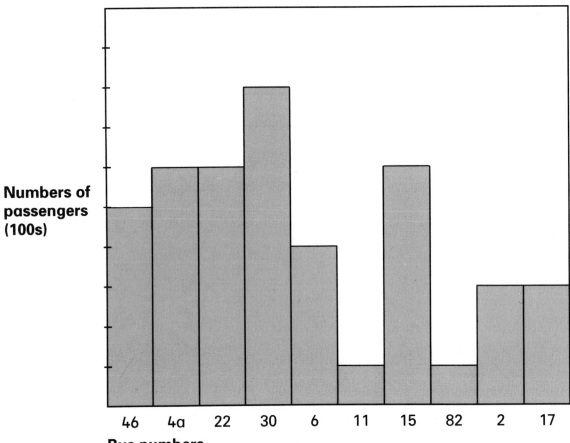

Numbers of passengers (100s)

Bus numbers: 46, 4a, 22, 30, 6, 11, 15, 82, 2, 17

100 children want to be .... when they grow up

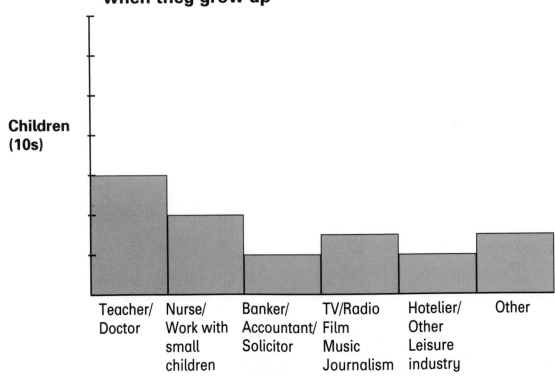

Children (10s)

Teacher/ Doctor | Nurse/ Work with small children | Banker/ Accountant/ Solicitor | TV/Radio Film Music Journalism | Hotelier/ Other Leisure industry | Other

Copymaster 94

Name _____

Bar chart – part drawn

Complete the bar chart

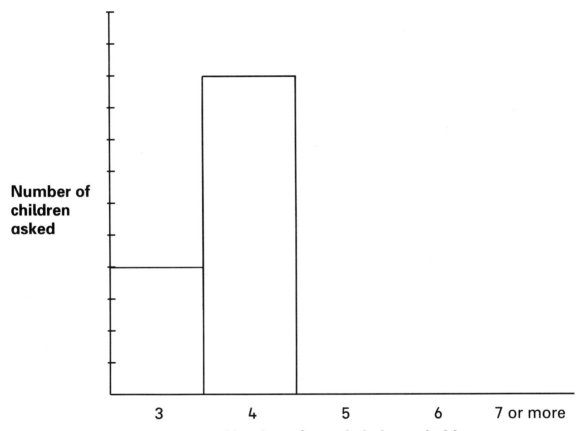

How many people live in your house?

Number of children asked

Number of people in household

Alison
Mark
Zelda
Muhammed   } 5 people each in their households
Suchita
Beatrice
Pauline

Deng
Crispin   } 6 people each in their households
Diamond

Lana   } 7 people in her household
Tolly   } 8 people in his household

Copymaster 95

Name _____

Pictograms

Sailings from the mainland to the Isle of Sun

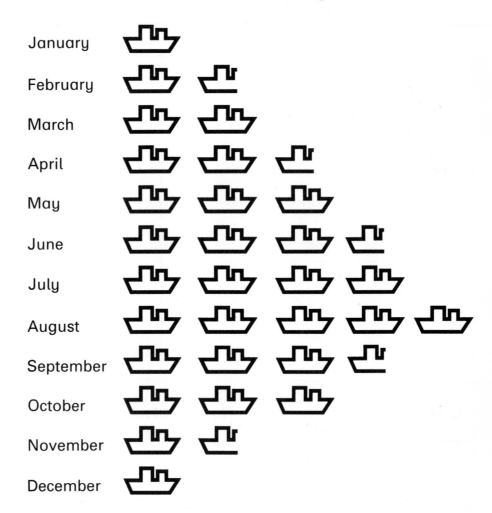

6 sailings	3 sailings

January
February
March
April
May
June
July
August
September
October
November
December

Frequency of wearing a cardigan or sweater at 10 am on each of 5 days.

2 people

Sample 30 children

Monday
Tuesday
Wednesday
Thursday
Friday

Copymaster 96

Name _____

Frequency data

Number of drinks bought in a motorway cafe in a day

| Tea | ||||\||\|||||| |||||||||||||| ||||
Coffee																						
Milk	||||||||||||||||
Squash	||||||||||||
Milk shake	||||||||||||||||||||||
Cola																																	
Spring water	||||||||||||||

Destinations of calls through a telephone exchange in an hour

London	56	Durham	2
Manchester	10	Exeter	4
Liverpool	16	Winchester	8
Birmingham	28	Brighton	2
Bristol	10	Cardiff	22

Observation report form

Name

Study to find out ....

....

Observations made/problem encountered

Evaluation/areas for modification

Pie charts

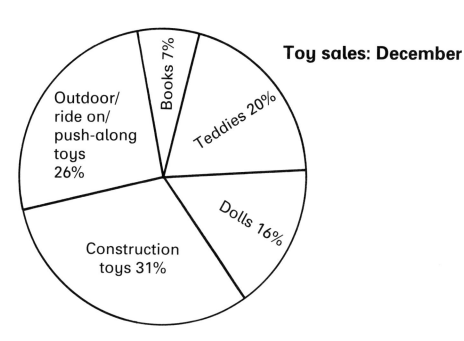

Toy sales: December

Outdoor/ride on/push-along toys 26%

Books 7%

Teddies 20%

Dolls 16%

Construction toys 31%

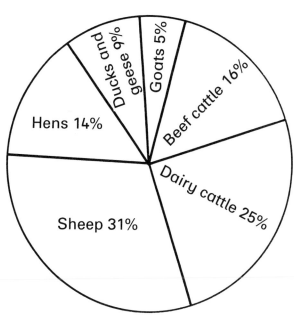

**Farming livestock held
in the county of Daleshire**

Goats 5%

Ducks and geese 9%

Beef cattle 16%

Hens 14%

Dairy cattle 25%

Sheep 31%

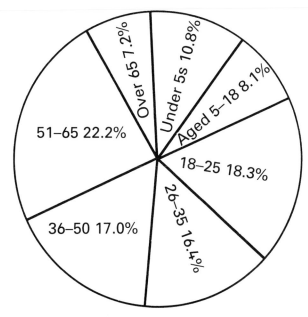

**Population breakdown
for town of Rightwhich**

Over 65 7.2%

Under 5s 10.8%

Aged 5–18 8.1%

51–65 22.2%

18–25 18.3%

36–50 17.0%

26–35 16.4%

Copymaster 99

Name _____

Possible happenings

Extremely unlikely	Unlikely	Likely	Very likely indeed

1 Eight-year-old boys take size 2 shoes.
2 All children like ice cream.
3 There is a rainbow when the sun shines while it is raining.
4 The first windy day of the month falls on a Friday.
5 Pencils break when you press hard on the point.
6 A poor diet affects your health.
7 If we grew our fingernails we would be very good at climbing trees.
8 Two people in your class have the same birthday.
9 You will win a prize this year.

How likely are these? Put their numbers on the line where you think they go.

Name _____

Probability scale

1 ⊤

Red lollies taste of raspberries?

Snow next winter?

Other life in the Universe?

Cats eat mice?

Flying arms?

Fluorescent ears?

0 ⊥

Copymaster 101

Coin toss/die throw

Coin toss results

Throw	Heads	Tails
1		
2		
3		
4		
5		
6		
7		
8		
9		
10		

Die throw results

Outcomes

Throw	1	2	3	4	5	6

Conversion

Where the conversion was found	Some comparisons in both units of measurement		Comments/discussion points

Name _____

Record sheet ▷

Pupil's name _____

	1	2	3	4
	5	6	7	8
	9	10	11	12
	13	14	15	16
	17	18	19	20
	21	22	23	24
	25	26	27	28
	29	30	31	32
Number	33	34	35	36
	37	38	39	40
	41	42	43	44
	45	46	47	48
	49	50	51	52
	53	54	55	56
	57	58	59	60
	61	62	63	64
	65	66	67	68
	69	70	71	72
Shape Space and Measures	73	74	75	76
	77	78	79	80
	81	82	83	84
	85	86	87	88
	89	90	91	92
	93	94	95	96
Handling data	97	98	99	100
	101	102	103	104
	105			
Resource Copymasters	RC1	RC2	RC3	RC4
	RC5	RC6	RC7	RC8
	RC9			

Copymaster 104

Name _____

Record sheet

Pupil's name _____

	1	2	3	4
Number	5	6	7	8
	9	10	11	12
	13	14	15	16
	17	18	19	20
	21	22	23	24
	25	26	27	28
	29	30	31	32
	33	34	35	36
	37	38	39	40
	41	42	43	44
	45	46	47	48
	49	50	51	52
	53	54	55	56
	57	58	59	60
	61	62	63	64
Shape Space and Measures	65	66	67	68
	69	70	71	72
	73	74	75	76
	77	78	79	80
	81	82	83	84
	85	86	87	88
Handling data	89	90	91	92
	93	94	95	96
	97	98	99	100
	101	102	103	104
	105			
Resource Copymasters	RC1	RC2	RC3	RC4
	RC5	RC6	RC7	RC8
	RC9			

Name _____

10 × 10 grid

100 squares

1	2	3	4	5	6	7	8	9	10
11	12	13	14	15	16	17	18	19	20
21	22	23	24	25	26	27	28	29	30
31	32	33	34	35	36	37	38	39	40
41	42	43	44	45	46	47	48	49	50
51	52	53	54	55	56	57	58	59	60
61	62	63	64	65	66	67	68	69	70
71	72	73	74	75	76	77	78	79	80
81	82	83	84	85	86	87	88	89	90
91	92	93	94	95	96	97	98	99	100

1	2	3	4	5	6	7	8	9	10
11	12	13	14	15	16	17	18	19	20
21	22	23	24	25	26	27	28	29	30
31	32	33	34	35	36	37	38	39	40
41	42	43	44	45	46	47	48	49	50
51	52	53	54	55	56	57	58	59	60
61	62	63	64	65	66	67	68	69	70
71	72	73	74	75	76	77	78	79	80
81	82	83	84	85	86	87	88	89	90
91	92	93	94	95	96	97	98	99	100

Name _____

Graph paper (2mm/10mm/20mm)

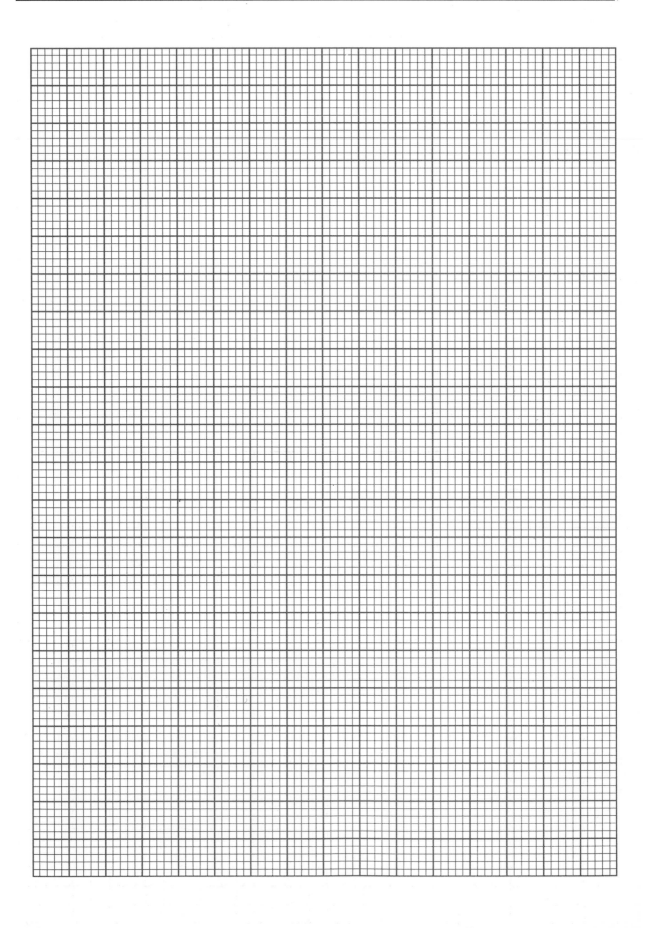

Name _____

Half-centimetre squared paper

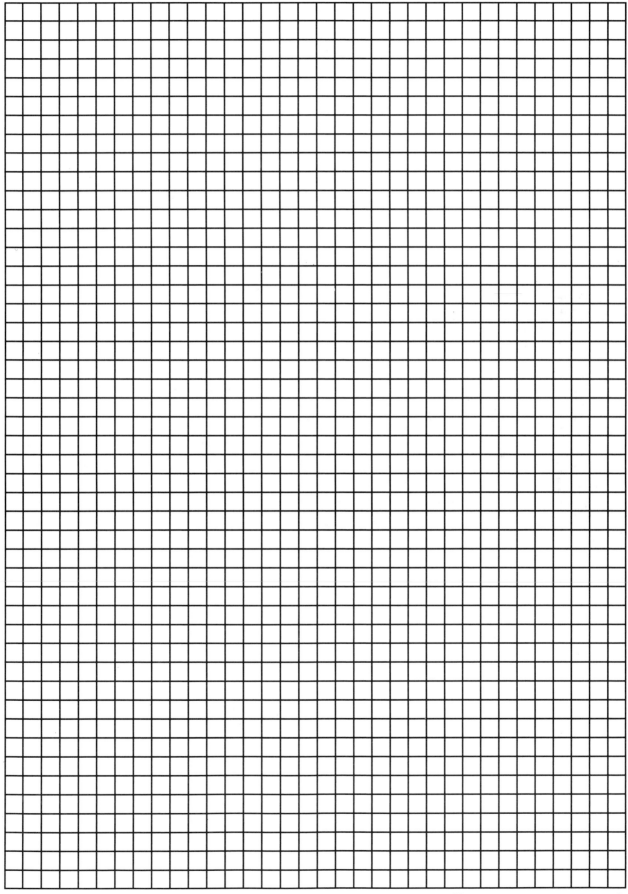

Block graph squares

Name _____

Dotty paper (1)

Name _____

Dotty paper (2)

Name _____

Isometric paper

Name _____

Regular hexagons paper

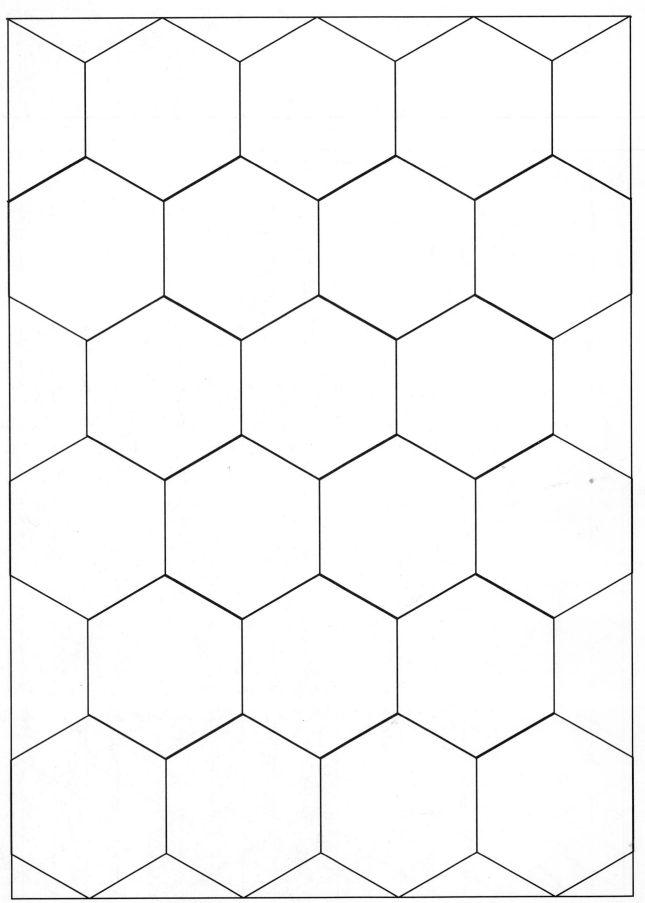